I'll Lend You My Daddy

Written by Becky King
Illustrated by Valerie Valdivia

STARTS WITH US

CHICAGO

Special thanks to my publisher Cynthea Liu, the Starts With Us team, illustrator Valerie Valdivia, and Erin O'Brien, my best friend of forty years, who has supported me through thick and thin.

I'd also like to thank the military families of Sara Lewis Holmes, Trent Reedy, Kay Pluta, Nancy Walter Eastman, Brad Olsen and Angela Dahle for their help with the book. Thank you also to the Staleys, the Morrisons, the Eubanks, and so many more military families that make sacrifices every day.

Starts With Us
An imprint of Pivotal Publishing

Chicago, Illinois

Illustrations © 2020 Starts With Us Inc.
Cover Design © 2020 Starts With Us Inc.

Paperback edition ISBN: 978-1-7336630-1-4
Hardcover edition ISBN: 978-1-7336630-3-8
E-book edition ISBN: 978-1-7336630-2-1

Library of Congress Control Number: 2019954924

Printed in the United States of America

For my son, Benson,

who has the biggest heart and makes me proud every day.

For my husband, Steve,

a man who has served for over thirty-five years,
my officer and a gentleman.

For my father, Dennis,

a retired firefighter and a former Marine.

In memory of my mother, Lynn Reed,

a teacher of over thirty years who loved reading
books to her students and me.

I'll lend you my daddy.
He works for us all.

He keeps the world safe
And answers our call.

I'll lend you my daddy.
He serves us, you see.

He's going away,
But he'll come back to me.

I'll lend you my daddy,
He's ready to go.

I'll try to be brave,
But I'll sure miss him so.

I'll lend you my daddy.
It's hard the first night.
Dinner without him
Just doesn't feel right.

I'll lend you my daddy.
My mom reminds me
Daddy must help,
So our land can be free.

I'll lend you my daddy.
There's a lot that I do.

There's soccer …

... gymnastics ...

He's missing this, too.

I'll lend you my daddy.
It seems like so long
Since he's read me a story
Or sung me a song.

I'll lend you my daddy.

My birthday is here.

I'm still a bit sad.

My father's not near.

I'll lend you my daddy.
I'm feeling so blue.
Mommy comes up
With something to do.

I'll lend you my daddy.
I know what to make.
I'll send him a package
And some of the cake!

I'll lend you my daddy.
His gift is complete.

A letter, some drawings,
And Dad's favorite treat!

I'll lend you my daddy.
I wave happily.

He adores all the goodies
And pictures of me.

I'll lend you my daddy.
He hung what I drew.

It reminds him of home.
He's missing me, too.

I'll lend you my daddy,
Although we're apart,
We're always a family
Close to his heart.

I'll lend you my daddy.
I mark off each day.
It won't be that long
Till he's on his way.

I'll lend you my daddy.
With markers and glue,
I'll make a great banner
In red, white, and blue.

I'll lend you my daddy.
I'll cheer for him, proud.
When he arrives,
I'll stick out from the crowd.

I'll lend you my daddy.
I'm lucky, you see.
All of his bravery
Has passed down to me!

I'll lend you my daddy.
My heart's beating fast.
I jump in his arms.

I hug him at last!

I'll lend you my daddy.
By air, land, or sea,

He's a true superhero
Who protects you and me.

I'll lend you my daddy.
I'm sure you'll agree.
Now that he's home,
He belongs just to me!

CPSIA information can be obtained
at www.ICGtesting.com
Printed in the USA
BVHW011649170423
662505BV00006B/71